Mexican
and other

Dragon
An imprint of the Children's Division
of the Collins Publishing Group
8 Grafton Street, London W1X 3LA

Published by Dragon Books 1987

ISBN 0-583-31142-3

Printed and bound in Great Britain by
Collins, Glasgow

Set in Century Schoolbook

STEVE TROTT

Mexican on a Bicycle and other crazy doodles

DRAGON

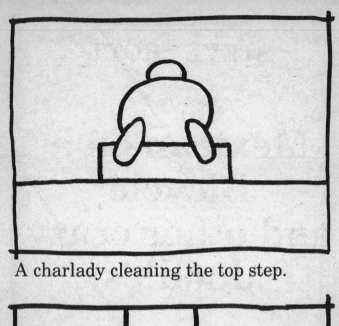

A charlady cleaning the top step.

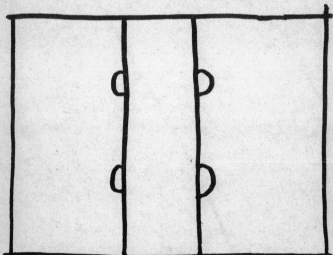

A koala bear climbing a tree.

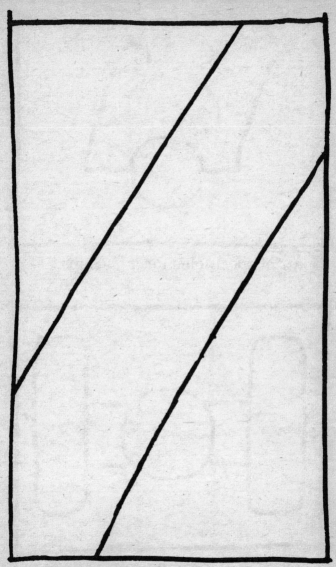

A giraffe going past the window.

A pair of spectacles for a Cyclops.

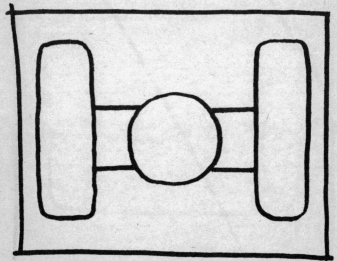

Rear view of a racing car . . . or aerial view of a railway porter.

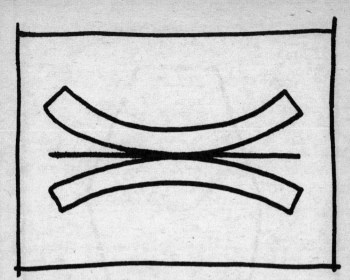

A week old cheese sandwich.

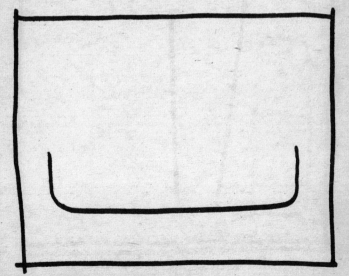

A comb for a bald man.

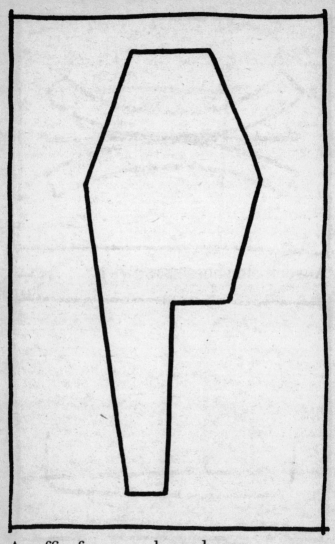

A coffin for a one-legged man.

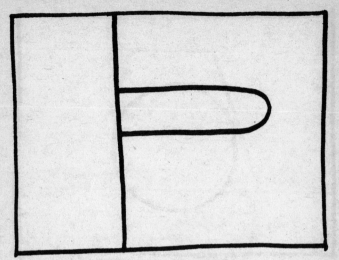

A trombonist in a phone box.

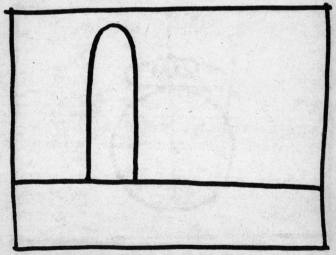

A trombonist in the bath.

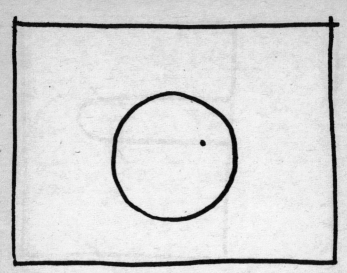

A fly on a bald man's head.

Aerial view of a bald man eating a hot dog.

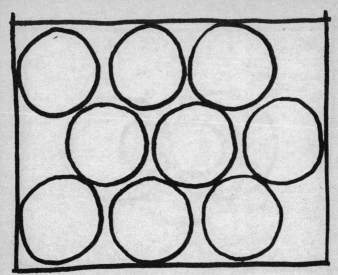

Several bald men in a lift.

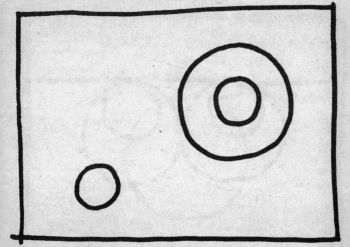

A bald Mexican's hat blowing off.

Two people whispering.

Two people leaning against a wall.

Two people arguing

Aerial view of a bus queue.

Close up of a zebra.

Negative of a zebra.

Zebra crossing a zebra crossing.

A witch walking in front of the Pyramids.

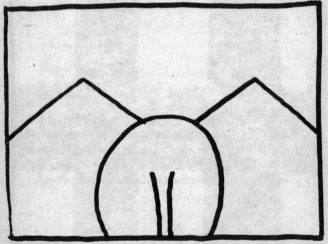

An elephant walking towards the Pyramids.

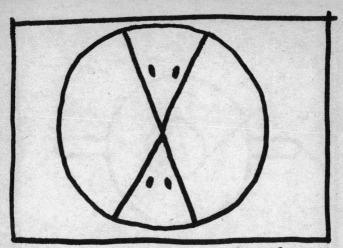

The last thing pussy saw when the mice threw him down the well.

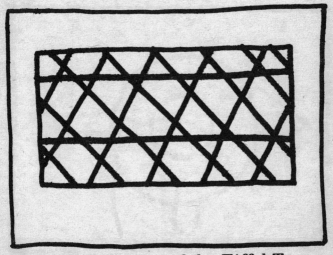

Tank driver's view of the Eiffel Tower.

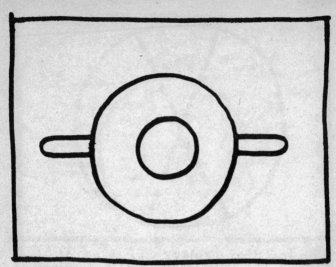

Aerial view of a Mexican on a bicycle.

A Mexican on a bicycle, turning left.

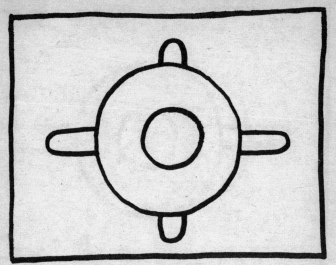

Look, no hands!

A Mexican frying an egg.

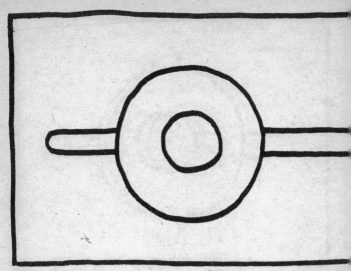

Two Mexicans on a tandem.

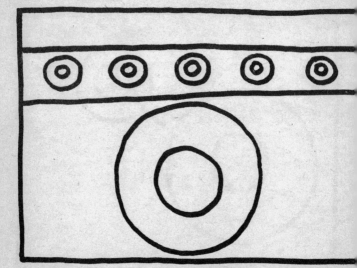

A Mexican watching a conveyor belt of doughnuts.

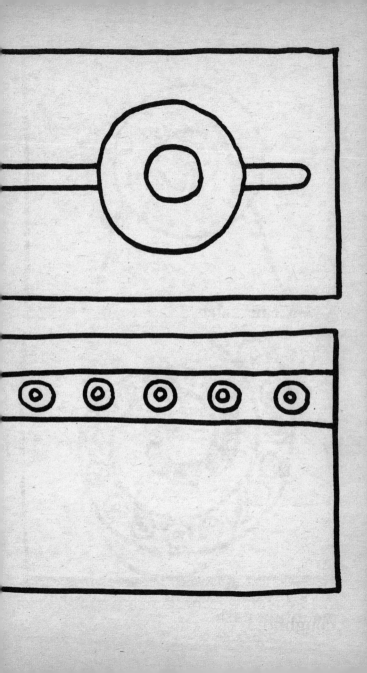

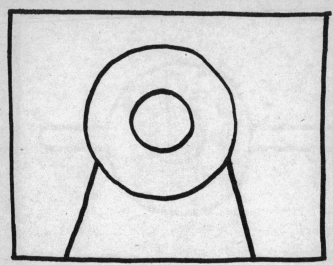

A Mexican, asleep.

An army of Mexicans going down a mountain path.

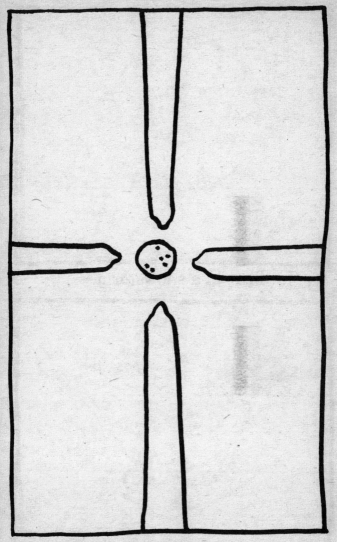

Four elephants sniffing a bun.

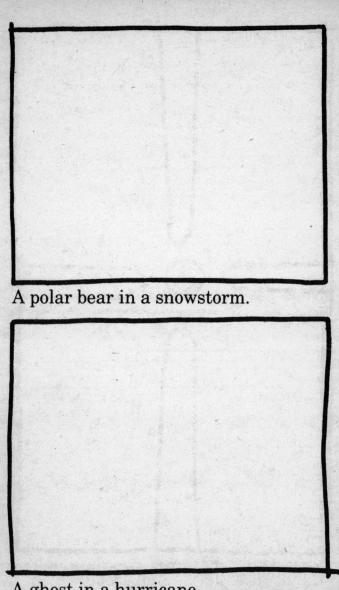

A polar bear in a snowstorm.

A ghost in a hurricane.

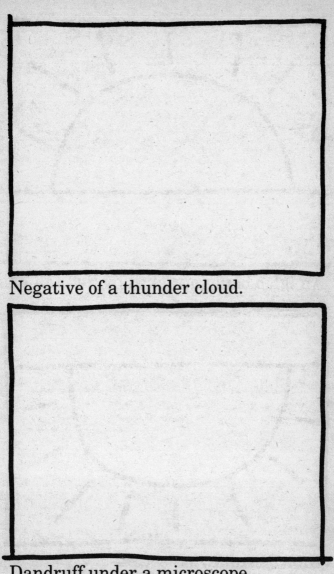

Negative of a thunder cloud.

Dandruff under a microscope.

An igloo being attacked by Red Indians.

An Australian sunset.

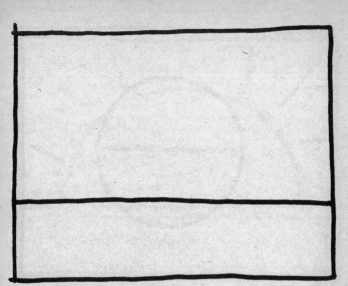

Close up of a vicar.

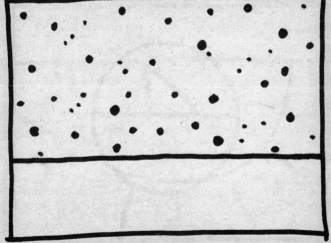

Close up of a vicar with measles.

The sea through a periscope.

A shark through a periscope.

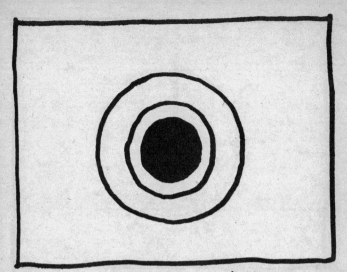

A shark staring into a periscope.

A shark eating a periscope.

If we start with this . . .

. . . add an oblong and we've got a music stand.

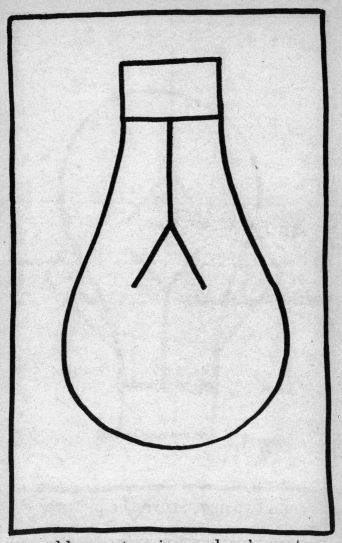

. . . add an outer ring and we've got a light bulb.

. . . add two arms, turn the picture upside down, and we've got a woman standing in a bowl of water, looking for the soap.

A ship arriving too late to save a drowning witch.

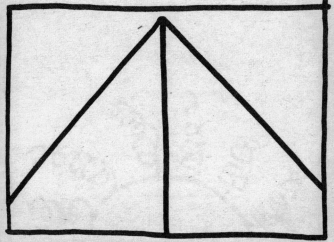

The last thing the witch saw as the ship ran her down.

A bald hedgehog.

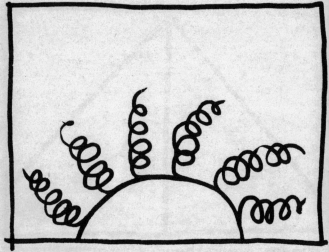

A hedgehog with a perm.

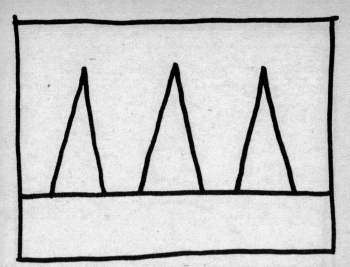

Three witches behind a wall.

Three witches looking into a cauldron.

A lonely germ.

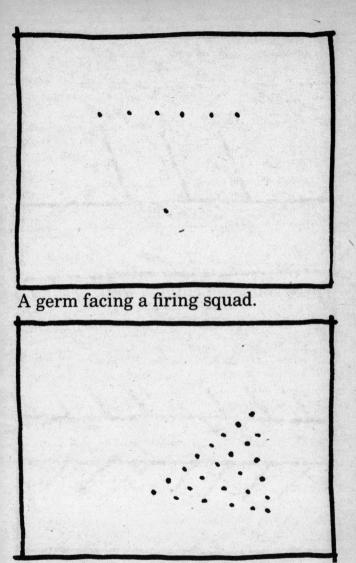

A germ facing a firing squad.

Germs flying south for the winter.

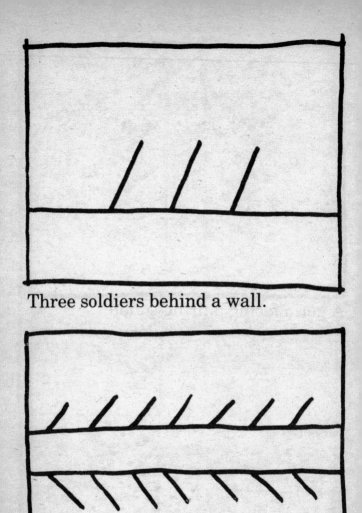

Three soldiers behind a wall.

Aerial view of the boat race.

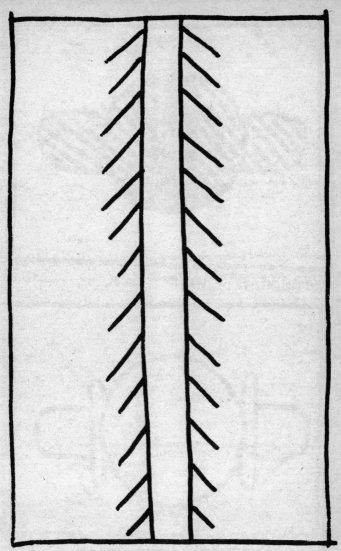

Close up of a gnat's leg.

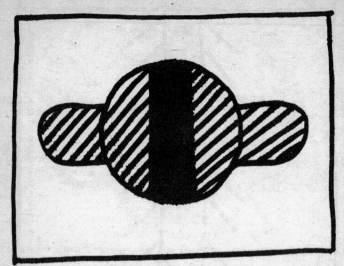

Aerial view of Mr T.

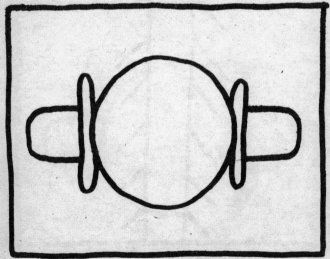

Aerial view of Prince Charles.

Aerial view of Barry Manilow.

Aerial view of Kojak.

Close up of Barry Manilow, head back
and singing.

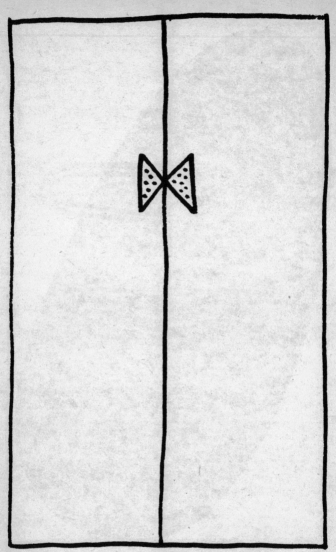

Sir Robin Day, caught in a lift.

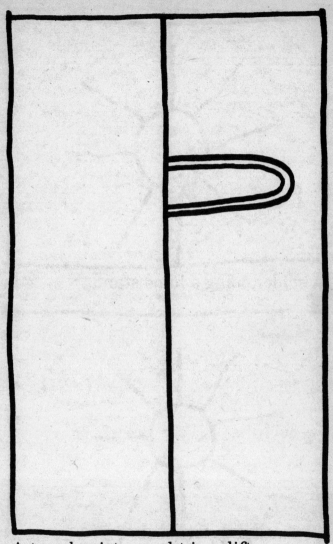

A trombonist, caught in a lift.

A spider doing a hand stand.

A spider on a skateboard.

A spider doing some weight-lifting.

Two spiders shaking hands.

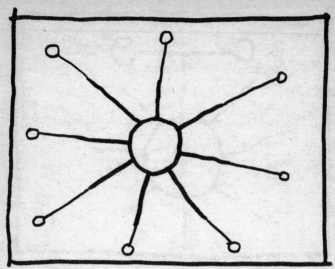

A spider playing with eight yo-yos.

The last thing the spider saw after being washed down the plug-hole.

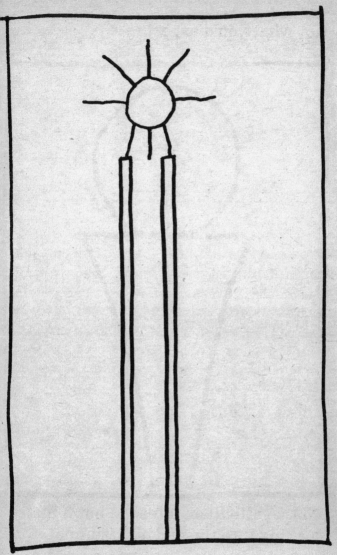

A spider on stilts.

Not what you'd expect . . .

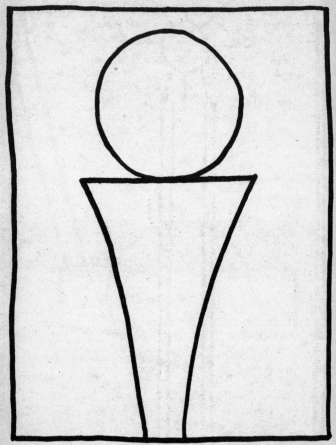

Not a golfball on a tee . . . but a man
looking into the end of a trumpet.

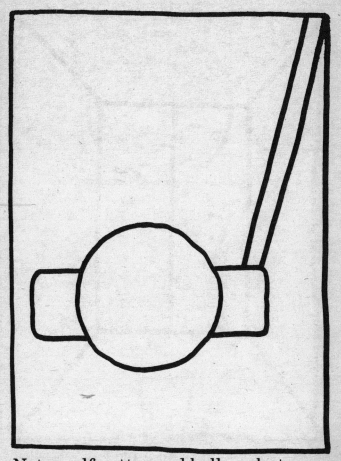

Not a golf putter and ball . . . but an
aerial view of a man with a rake.

Not what you'd expect . . .

Not a bird seen from a prison cell . . .
but the shadow of a seagull dive-
bombing a tent.

Aerial view of a Mexican with a
Martini in one hand and a sausage on
a stick in the other.

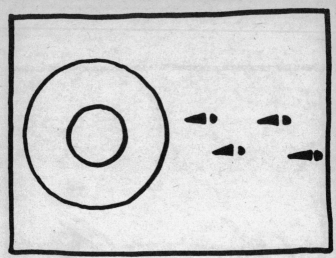

A Mexican walking in the desert.

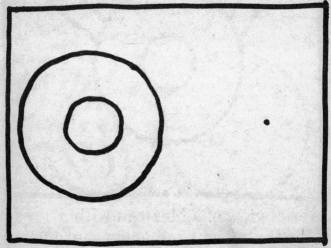

A Mexican spitting out a grape pip.

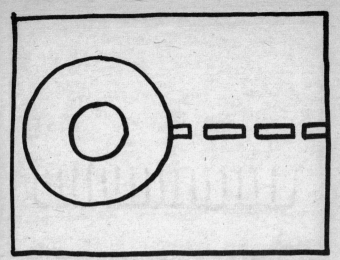

A Mexican painting lines in the road.

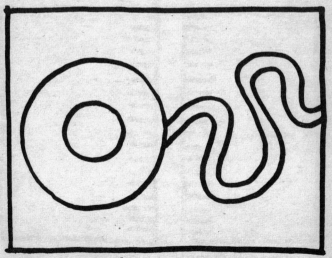

A drunk Mexican painting lines in the road.

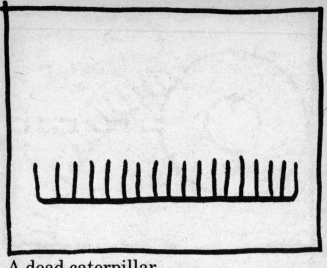

A dead caterpillar.

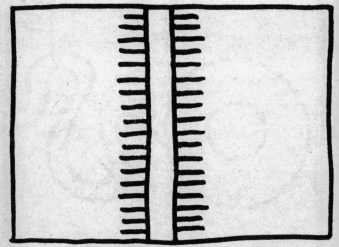

A caterpillar walking down your glasses.

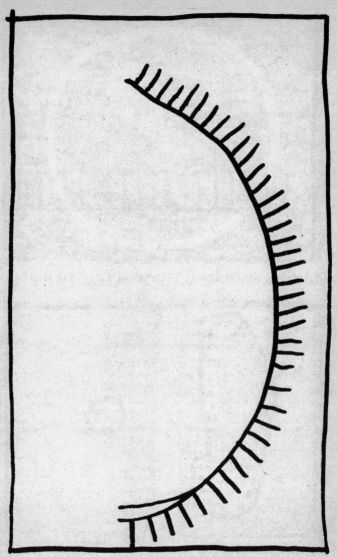

A caterpillar doing a handstand.

Life as seen by a worm living in a beer c

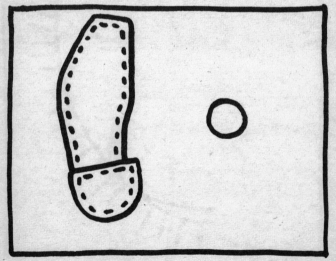

Worm's eye view of Long John Silver.

Worm's eye view of a cow.

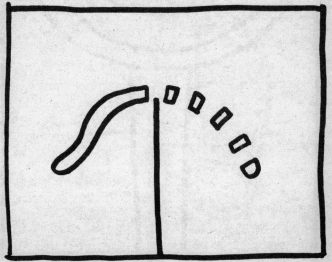

Worm climbing over a razor-blade.

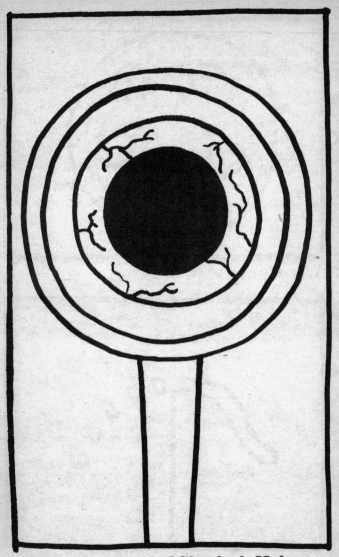

Worm's eye view of Sherlock Holmes.

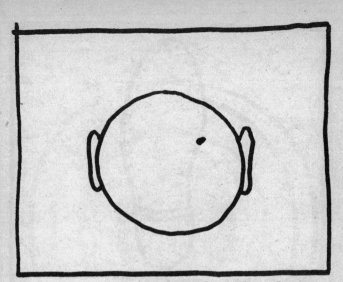

An ant on Prince Charles's head.

Ants playing leap frog.

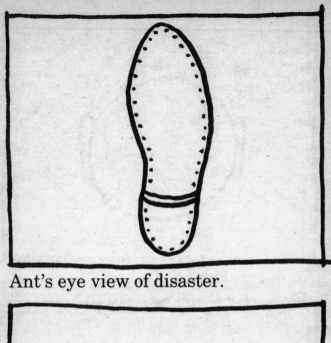

Ant's eye view of disaster.

An ant on a tight-rope.

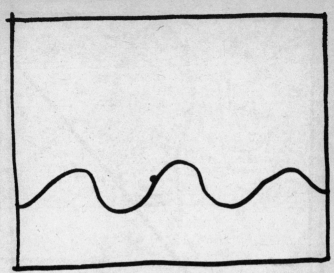

An ant swimming the Channel.

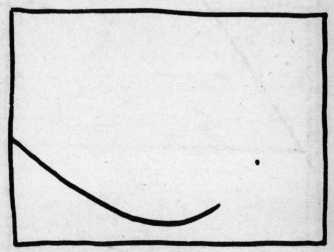

An ant ski-jumping.

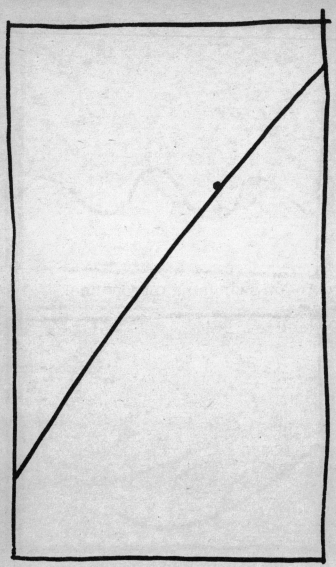

An ant climbing a mountain.

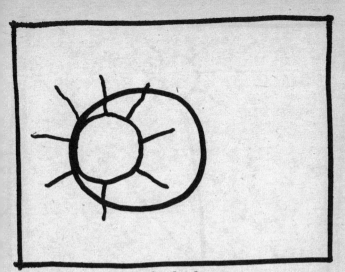

A spider with a hula-hoop.

A spider blowing bubble-gum.

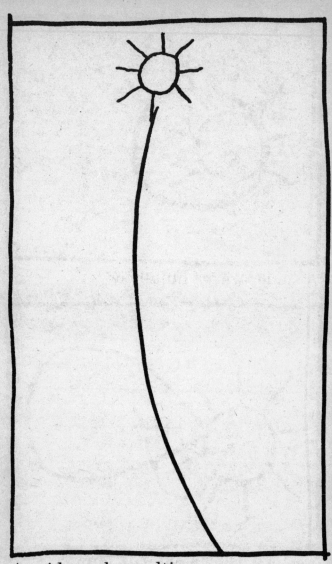

A spider pole-vaulting.

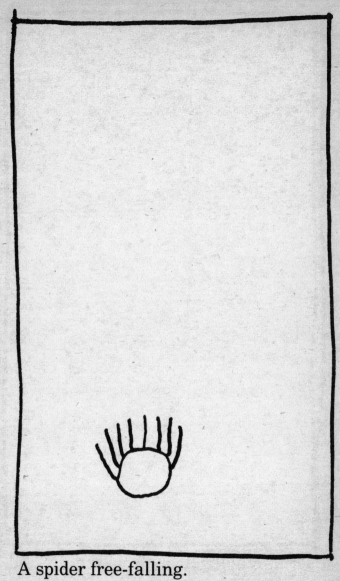

A spider free-falling.

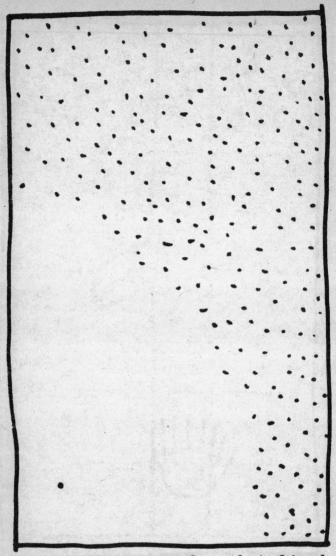

Germs staying away from their friend,
who has caught penicillin.

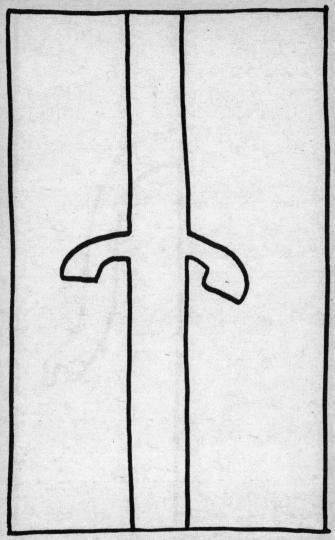

An ostrich swallowing a telephone.

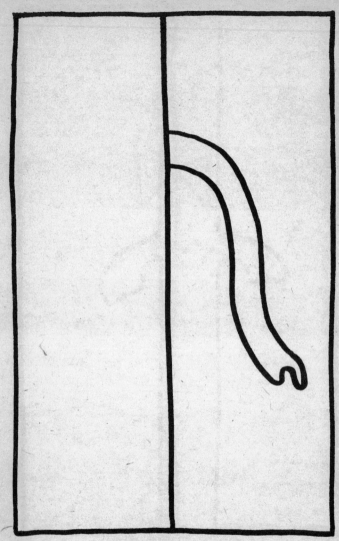

An elephant caught in a lift.

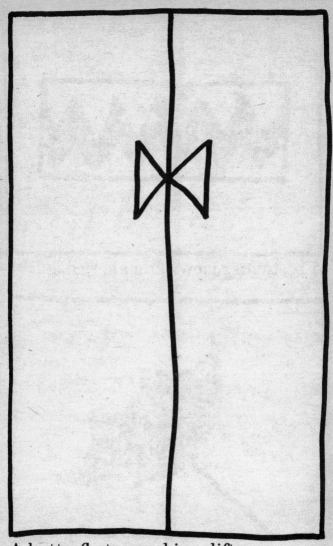

A butterfly trapped in a lift.

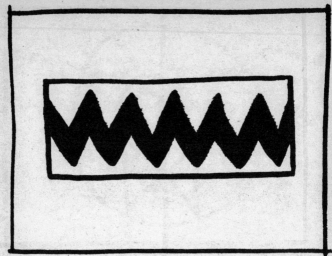

A postman's view of an angry dog.

An umbrella on a windy day.

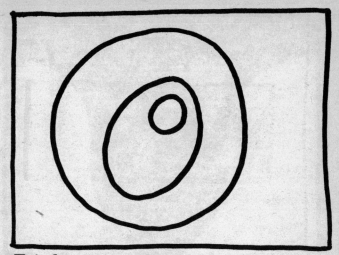

Fried egg on a plate.

Poached egg on toast.

Two people nearly touching noses . . .
or is it a vase?

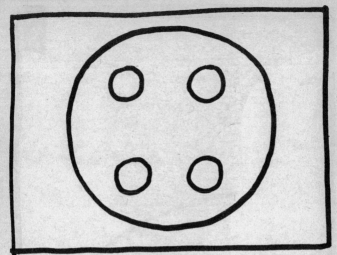

An elephant hiding upside down in a
bowl of custard.

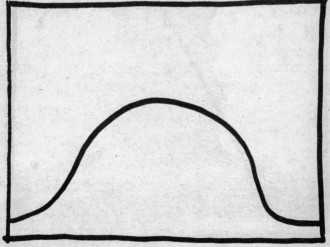

An elephant hiding in a tent.

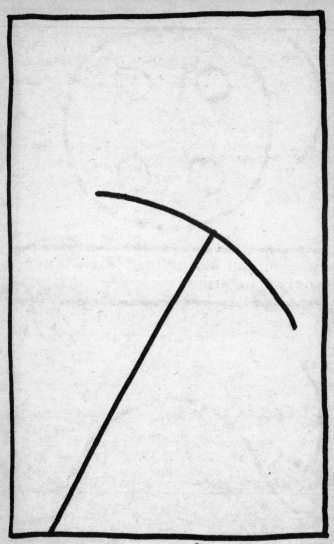

A man digging a trench.

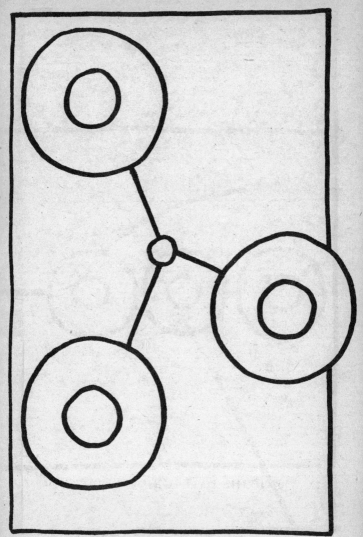

Three Mexicans around a maypole.

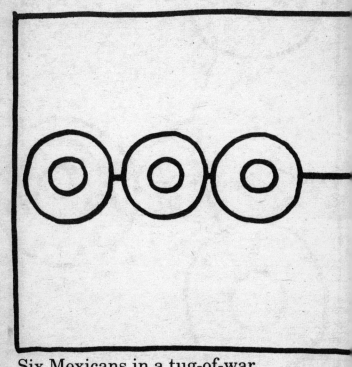

Six Mexicans in a tug-of-war.

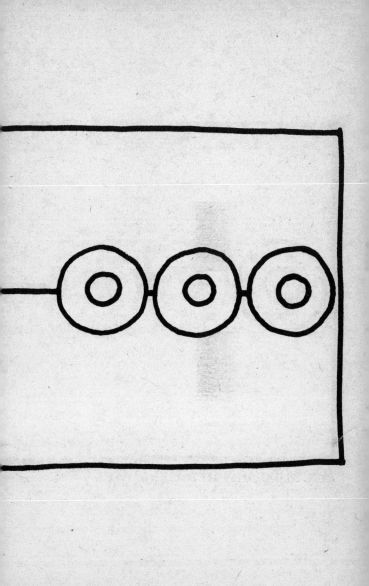